Road of Amendments

A Children's Novel

Road of Amendments
A Children's Novel
Copyright © 2021 by Amelie Zuberi

Additional copies may be ordered from the publisher for educational, business, promotional or premium use.
For information, contact ALIVE Book Publishing at: alivebookpublishing.com, or call (925) 837-7303.

ISBN 13
978-1-63132-154-2 Paperback
978-1-63132-157-3 Hardcover

Library of Congress Control Number: 2021923172

Library of Congress Cataloging-in-Publication Data
is available upon request.

First Edition

Published in the United States of America by ALIVE Book Publishing and ALIVE Publishing Group, imprints of Advanced Publishing LLC
3200 A Danville Blvd., Suite 204, Alamo, California 94507
alivebookpublishing.com

PRINTED IN THE UNITED STATES OF AMERICA

10 9 8 7 6 5 4 3 2 1

Road of Amendments

A Children's Novel

Amelie Zuberi

Alive Book Publishing

To Kaela,
who stuck by me through this Process,

and Mom,
who encouraged me

When I sat down and decided to write a book, I wanted to write about something relevant to people's lives. I wanted to help educate people on complex ideas. The United States Constitution states the fundamental rights of American citizens, but most citizens don't know their rights. I wrote this book to address that issue and help young readers understand their rights as United States citizens. To do this, I divided the first ten amendments into ten chapters. In order to explain them each chapter has a story that relates to the amendment. I hope these stories help people in understanding the first ten amendments of the United States Constitution.

~ Amelie Zuberi

The 1st Amendment

Congress shall make no law respecting an establishment of religion, or prohibiting the free exercise thereof; or abridging the freedom of speech, or the press; or the right of the people peaceably to assemble, and to petition the Government for a redress of grievances.

When she got to history class later that day, her teacher was writing something on the board. Mrs. Hansen had written in big bold letters: "The United States Constitution."

"For our next unit, we are going to become experts on the Constitution," she told them.

Hazel groaned inwardly. She hated units like this one and the Constitution was so boring.

A bunch of old guys wrote it forever ago, why does it matter? She thought to herself. Honestly, it doesn't matter. It's not like I am ever going to use it.

Mrs. Hansen continued talking about why the Constitution was written but Hazel wasn't listening.

"The first amendment of the constitution is *'Congress shall make no law respecting an establishment of religion, or prohibiting the free exercise thereof; or abridging the freedom of speech, or the press; or the right of the people peaceably to assemble, and to petition the Government for a redress of grievances.'* Can anyone tell me what that means?"

Hazel tuned her out and started thinking of all the fun activities she and her friends were going to do after school. They were going to have a blast!

"Hazel?" Mrs. Hansen abruptly said, interrupting her thoughts.

"Um…..sorry what?"

"I was asking, do you know what this amendment means?"

Hazel tried to think. It said something about religion and speech. . . Right?

"Hazel, pay attention, I have asked you the question twice now."

Hazel winced. Oops.

"I am sorry, but I don't know," Hazel told her.

"Okay, does anyone else know?" Mrs. Hansen's eyes scanned the room to see no hands raised. "Well then, for your homework I want you to write two paragraphs describing what it means. Don't forget to do some research! Class dismissed."

Hazel rushed out of class and raced to her locker. Just as she got there, she heard shouting from the end of the hall. She found a group of students clustered around the announcement board.

"Can you believe it? They can't just do that. This is so unfair," one of the girls whined.

"You can't believe what? What's so unfair?" Hazel cut in.

"You haven't heard?" the girl pointed at a flyer that was pinned on the board.

From next Friday,
All pizza days shall be canceled
due to limited resources

Hazel's heart dropped. Pizza days were canceled! Pizza was the only food that the students enjoyed in the cafeteria that was famous for serving bland food with no flavor.

"Just like that? Seriously, that's all the information they give us?! UGHHH," Hazel groaned.

'That's exactly what we all are thinking! I know right. Exactly," came the chorus of responses.

—

"Dad, it's just so unfair. I mean, pizza is the only good thing in that cafeteria and now they are discontinuing it and they gave us NO information at all. I swear I hate this school," Hazel exclaimed across the dinner table.

"Hazel, honey, calm down. I understand that you think this is unfair, but try to look at both sides. If you still think this is unfair and cruel, do something about it. That is what the first amendment is for, am I right?" he said with a wink.

He got up and kissed Hazel on the head, walking to his office. Hazel sat there dumbfounded. She scrambled to her room and looked up the first amendment. A particular phrase caught her eye: *"the right of the people peaceably to assemble, and to petition the Government for a redress of grievances."* Hazel realized what her dad meant. She and her classmates were the people and her school was the government. It was her right as a citizen to exercise her first amendment right.

She re-read the text a couple of times and an idea began to spark. She switched tabs and composed an email to her classmates...

As you all probably know by now, pizza days at school have been canceled. All of us have been understandably distressed, so I decided we should do something about it. I want to organize a protest if you all will join me. I was talking to my dad and he mentioned the first amendment. The first amendment states that this is fully within our rights. That we have the right to protest. We all firmly believe that pizza days should be maintained and we demonstrate that we are willing to fight for that!

Before she could regret it, Hazel pressed send and lay back in her chair with a smile on her face.

The 2nd Amendment

A well regulated Militia, being necessary to the security of a free State, the right of the people to keep and bear Arms, shall not be infringed.

Hazel stumbled out of the bus, head spinning with numbers, dates, and textbook images. As she reached her room something caught her eye. It was the book she had recently bought: *The Year's Hunter.* Hazel picked it up and became immersed in the story:

I looked around at the sparse kitchen and yelled out to my family.

"I'm going out. We have no meat for dinner."

I grabbed my gun off the wall and walked out. I started to move deeper into the forest when I heard a sound. I quickly started to follow it and it led to a great big stag. I aimed my gun and took the shot.

Hazel squeezed her eyes shut. Why did the main character have to go hunting? She hated that. That poor stag. It's not like Hazel could just grab a gun and start killing animals. At that Hazel paused. Wait a second. How did the character even have access to the gun?

Hazel continued to contemplate. Why did he even need a gun in the first place? She had always been told that guns were dangerous and this guy just had one in this house! What was going on?!

The more Hazel thought about it the more curious she

became. Finally, she went downstairs to ask someone.

She found her dad sitting in the living room.

"Dad, can you help me with something?" Hazel went on to explain the book and her questions.

"Well Hazel, it all boils down to the second amendment, which says that you have the right to bear arms. Or in other words, have guns," her dad explained.

"But Dad, why?"

"Well, when the U.S. was separating from Britain they wanted to be able to create their own military to defend themselves. They didn't want to be unable to protect themselves in case the government tried to take over. They didn't want to be defenseless against a tyrannical federal government."

"That makes sense, given what happened with Britain. What about hunting, like in my book?"

"Well, back when the United States gained its freedom, people had to hunt for food, and guns made that a lot easier."

After hearing her dad's explanation, she began to calm down. What her dad was saying showed how different those times were and how people's lives back then were different from hers. And although her family didn't need to hunt for food, having the right to bear arms to ensure liberty was logical and made a lot of sense.

"Okay, that makes A LOT more sense. Thanks, Dad!"

"Of course."

Hazel walked away from the living room satisfied and picked her book back up.

I grabbed the heavy deer and started to drag it home, happy that I was bringing something home for dinner . . .

The 3rd Amendment

No Soldier shall, in time of peace be quartered in any house, without the consent of the Owner, nor in time of war, but in a manner to be prescribed by law.

Finally! Hazel had just finished her homework and finally had time to read her new book. It was so interesting. She propped it open.

I was currently hiding in my room, unsuccessfully ignoring my "guest." When will this cursed revolution end?

"Hey. I am hungry. Get in here and make me some dinner," I heard from the other room.

I sighed. Oh, God. Help me. I can't stand that guy. I slowly stood up, straightened my dress, and walked into the other room.

"How can I help you, sir?" I asked quietly, my eyes pinned to the floor.

"Are you deaf? I want to eat. Make me something."

*Anger sparked in me. I was **not** a servant. How dare he? This was my house. He could not push me around.*

Yes. Yes. Yes. She was finally going to put that soldier in his place. Hazel put down the book and did a little victory dance. Ever since the beginning of the book, this annoying soldier had been bossing her aroundw. Hazel eagerly picked up the book and resumed reading.

Then reality hit me. In all truth, he could do whatever he wanted. I pushed down my anger. I made my way to the kitchen and rummaged through my meager supply of food. If this kept going on, I won't have anything to eat by the end of the week.

Are you kidding me? Hazel snapped her book shut, furious. Why on Earth was this soldier able to boss this poor lady around. He was even starving her! She started to pace her room, stomping her feet. If someone came into my house and started bossing me around, I would slap them, she thought. Although she was angry, Hazel was extremely curious. Where in the world was this book going? She eyed the book on her desk and snatched it up.

I quickly fixed together the best meal I could with my meager supplies. I put aside what would be generously called a slice of bread for myself. That would have to be enough. I made my way back to the soldier and set the meal in front of him. He eyed it with disdain.

"Is that all, sir?"

"Is this supposed to be dinner? This is barely enough to feed a mouse!" Anger was growing in his eyes.

"I am afraid that is all I have," I said, shrinking back.

"You useless girl. Nevermind. I am leaving to eat dinner with a friend. You better have something tomorrow."

With that, he scooped up the food and threw it in the trash, and left. I ran over to the trash bin and pulled the food out. I cleaned it off the best I could and stored it in the kitchen. I ate my dinner and retired to my room.

Hazel could not believe it. She hated this man more and more with every sentence. He could have at the very least gotten her some food. He was rich enough. Hazel continued reading until her dad poked his head in and told her to go to bed.

Even then as she lay in bed, she kept thinking about it. Why was this soldier able to boss the main character around, stay in her house, eat her food, and leave without any payment or gratitude? It was downright evil. Eventually, she was able to sleep, but this question kept nagging at the back of her mind.

—

Hazel walked into history class, her nose buried in her book. She was unable to put it down. She walked right past Mrs. Hansen without even noticing.

"Hazel?"

Startled, Hazel looked up to see Mrs. Hansen looking at her with an eyebrow raised.

She smiled sheepishly. Oops.

"Sorry, Mrs. Hansen. Good morning."

Mrs. Hansen laughed. "Good morning, Hazel. Good book?"

"Oh, yes. It's amazing."

Hazel went on about the book and the question that was nagging at her. She cut herself off.

"Oops, sorry for rambling."

"Don't be sorry. This will actually fit in very well with today's lesson," Mrs. Hansen said, amused.

Mrs. Hansen walked to the front of the class and cleared her throat. The class settled down.

"Good morning everyone. So Hazel was talking to me about a book she was reading and I realized it would tie very well into today's lesson. Hazel, would you mind telling them what you told me?"

Hazel, confused, explained.

Mrs. Hansen smiled and thanked her.

"Did you guys know that during colonial and revolutionary America, British soldiers stayed in civilians' houses? They were fed and looked after by American civilians. If Americans refused to house them it was considered treason. America back then was still a new place and there were few resources to spare. Understandably, Americans were not happy with this especially since these soldiers were here to make sure the British stayed in control," Mrs. Hansen told the class.

"This is why when Americans gained their freedom, they made sure the new citizens never felt the way they did before. This was the birth of the third amendment of the Constitution."

Mrs. Hansen turned around and wrote on the board.

"No Soldier shall, in time of peace be quartered in any house, without the consent of the Owner, nor in time of war, but in a manner to be prescribed by law."

"Mrs. Hansen, is this why in my book, the character couldn't turn the soldier away?" Hazel asked, excited.

"Yes. If she had, it would have been considered treason and she would be severely punished. But once the third amendment was created, she would have been able to turn him away without any consequences."

After school that day, Hazel had more understanding of her novel and eagerly opened it up. She couldn't wait to see where this book took her.

The 4th Amendment

The right of the people to be secure in their persons, houses, papers, and effects, against unreasonable searches and seizures, shall not be violated, and no Warrants shall issue, but upon probable cause, supported by Oath or affirmation, and particularly describing the place to be searched, and the persons or things to be seized.

Hazel was in science class when she heard an announcement over the speakers. She paused her work to listen.

"Hazel Miller, please report to Principal Winter's office."

Confused, she got up and gathered her things. As she was walking to the office, she racked her brain trying to come up with anything she had done wrong. When she checked into the front office, she was sent directly into Principal Winter's office.

Principal Winter looked up as she walked in.

"Ah, Hazel, come in. Have a seat."

"Hey, Principal Winter, can I ask why I'm here?"

"Of course. I just want to start by saying you are not in trouble. Yesterday afternoon after school ended we did a locker check. I don't know how to say this easily but we found the answer key to Mrs. Hansen's latest tests in one of your classmate's lockers. I was wondering if you knew anything about this. We are talking to everyone in their class. I am sure you know this is very serious."

Hazel furrowed her eyebrows. "Locker checks?"

"Um, yes. . ."

"You do locker checks?"

"Of course we do. To make sure something like this doesn't happen. Now Hazel, let's focus on the answer key."

"Principal Winter, you should not do locker checks. It's an invasion of our privacy."

"Hazel, dear, we must do locker checks. This is a school, not something out of a book."

"I'm sorry, but I won't stand for it!" Hazel exclaimed.

Principal Winter sighed and rubbed her head. "Would it make you feel better if I told you we had probable cause?" she asked.

"Probable cause. . .?"

"It means that we had enough evidence to search the lockers. Mrs. Hansen had told us that her answer key was missing, so we did a whole school search for them, including the lockers."

"So you had a good reason to search the lockers?"

"Yes," Principal Winter told her, laughing, "you kids are becoming justice-seeking lawyers."

Hazel laughed as well. "Well then if you have probable cause, let's get back to the answer key."

As Hazel walked back to class, she thought about how the amendments applied to her life more than she had assumed. She suddenly felt excited to go back to class and find more connections between the Constitution and her life.

The 5th Amendment

No person shall be held to answer for a capital, or otherwise infamous crime, unless on a presentment or indictment of a Grand Jury, except in cases arising in the land or naval forces, or in the Militia, when in actual service in time of War or public danger; nor shall any person be subject for the same offence to be twice put in jeopardy of life or limb; nor shall be compelled in any criminal case to be a witness against himself, nor be deprived of life, liberty, or property, without due process of law; nor shall private property be taken for public use, without just compensation.

Hazel was reading in her room when her dad came in.

"Hazel, have you done your chores yet?" he asked her.

"Um. . .yes," she responded hesitantly.

The truth was she hadn't. She had been so caught up in her book that she had completely forgotten.

"You don't sound too sure."

"I did it, now can I continue reading?"

Her dad laughed. "Of course."

She was only a few more pages in when she heard her parents call her downstairs. They were standing by a full trash can. A trash can that she was supposed to take out.

Oh no.

"Hazel, you were supposed to take the trash out," her mom told her.

"And even worse, you lied to me!" her dad added.

"Okay okay, I forgot and I had just gotten to a good part of my book and I didn't want to stop. So can I *please* go and finish it?"

With that Hazel left the room and went upstairs. Her parents called after her but she pretended not to hear them.

As she reopened her book, her mom came in.

"Hazel, you cannot leave your chores, lie to your dad, ignore us and expect there to be no punishment!"

"Oh come on. It wasn't that big of a deal!"

"Hazel, you can't do that. I'm grounding you. Go do your chores."

Hazel tried to protest but then thought better of it. She walked downstairs and took out the trash. When she came back inside, her dad was sitting on the couch.

"Hazel! Come over here," her dad called out.

Oh no. Hazel was seriously in trouble. She really regretted forgetting the simple task. She walked over to her dad.

"Dad, I'm sorry. I seriously just forgot and then the book . . . I didn't mean to lie to you."

"That doesn't change the fact that you did. You can't lie to us, Hazel. And since you lied there has to be a consequence. You can't go to Renya's house on Friday."

"What? That's not fair. I mean it's totally unconstitutional. You and Mom both gave me a punishment for the same thing. That's double jeopardy. I apologized and I will take one of the punishments but it's not fair to be grounded and not be able to go to Renya's house."

"Well, I didn't know that your mom gave you a punishment as well. I guess since you pulled the Constitution card I can let you go this time. But remember we are your parents and we deserve your respect. Also in the future, don't argue. It'll only make it worse," he said, laughing.

"Okay, promise," Hazel said, laughing as well.

The 6th Amendment

In all criminal prosecutions, the accused shall enjoy the right to a speedy and public trial, by an impartial jury of the State and district wherein the crime shall have been committed, which district shall have been previously ascertained by law, and to be informed of the nature and cause of the accusation; to be confronted with the witnesses against him; to have compulsory process for obtaining witnesses in his favor, and to have the Assistance of Counsel for his defense.

Hazel was walking towards the cafeteria when she heard yelling.

"IT'S MINE."

"NO, YOU STOLE IT!"

"I DIDN'T STEAL ANYTHING!"

Hazel spun around in the direction of the noise and saw two of her classmates, Edith and Mary, toe to toe. The usual best friends looked ready to rip each other's hair out. Hazel speed-walked down the hall, ready to stop a fight.

"Whoa, guys calm down. What's happening?" Hazel interjected.

They both started to speak at once and then stopped and glared at each other.

"Mary, why don't you explain. And Edith, let her talk,"

Hazel cut in.

"Well, Edith and I are in the same history class and we sit right next to each other. Now during class yesterday, Edith told me that she really liked my pens and wished she had them. My pens are super cool, my dad got them for me! I would recognize them anywhere. After class, I thought I had lost them, I looked everywhere for them and even asked Edith if she had seen them. She even offered to help me look for them! I thought that was nice of her but then today in class SHE TOOK OUT MY PEN AND STARTED USING IT. SHE STOLE IT!" Mary spat out the final words like venom.

"I'VE TOLD YOU A MILLION TIMES. I DIDN'T STEAL IT. I BOUGHT MY OWN YESTERDAY BECAUSE I LIKED YOURS," Edith shrieked.

Are they seriously starting World War Three over a pen, Hazel thought.

"Well, *Edith,* you can ask MY friends, they would agree with ME!"

"MY friends know I am telling the truth!"

"YOUR friends are wrong. Sybil, come tell her." Mary gestured to the student with long brown hair next to her.

"Piper agrees with ME." Edith brought her own friend forward who was previously standing near Hazel.

Then inspiration struck as Hazel thought back on the sixth amendment.

"*...The accused shall enjoy the right to a speedy and public trial, by an impartial jury...*"

Impartial juries, Hazel thought. She was struck by a sudden realization: this would not be a fair trial! Each of the friends being called over was biased in favor of her own friend.

Hazel cut in again. "I get that you are both upset but you need someone who is equally close to both people to settle this argument. Someone like the teachers! An impartial jury doesn't favor one side over the other, but your friends might. Mary, the friends that you are calling over are going to support you no matter what. And the same goes for your friends, Edith. You need someone who won't do that to make this fair. Mrs. Hansen taught us about this, the sixth amendment! Everyone has the right to a speedy trial by an impartial jury. Remember? "

Both girls thought about it and nodded.

"Fine, let's go find an impartial jury," Mary told Edith.

Edith made a noise of agreement and they both headed off.

Hazel smiled to herself, proud she could put her knowledge to use. She left her friends to resolve their argument fairly.

The 7th Amendment

In Suits at common law, where the value in controversy shall exceed twenty dollars, the right of trial by jury shall be preserved, and no fact tried by a jury, shall be otherwise re-examined in any Court of the United States, than according to the rules of the common law.

Hazel was sitting in English class struggling to keep her eyes open. She had barely slept the night before because her teacher, Mrs. Truffle, had assigned one of her infamously tedious homework assignments. Mrs. Truffle seemed unaffected by how listless her students were. She continued to assign more and more work, taking up more hours of the night. As she watched the notorious homework assigner prescribe yet another massive pile of paperwork, Hazel decided she could not take this anymore.

Once the bell rang, Hazel rose slowly and shuffled to Mrs. Truffle's desk, rubbing sleep from her eyes.

"Hey, Mrs. Truffle. I was wondering if you had a minute. I need to talk to you about something," Hazel mumbled tentatively.

Mrs. Truffle glanced up from her stack of papers. "Hmm, of course. What is it?"

"Well, it's about homework. I know you try your best

to keep it a good amount but lately you've been assigning way too much. I've been staying up till 1 am trying to finish it."

Mrs. Truffle rolled her eyes. "Well, it is not MY fault that you've been taking a long time to do it. I assign a perfectly reasonable amount of work. You must have been distracted."

"That's the thing, Mrs. Truffle, it's not that. It's the workload."

"Well I never, in all my years of teaching…"

Hazel could see the teacher begin to get heated, and she suddenly felt that she had made a mistake. As Mrs. Truffle carried on, her panic rose until Hazel felt struck by a sudden burst of inspiration. Just a few hours before, Mrs. Hansen had taught them about the seventh amendment. The right to have a trial by jury. Her mind raced to link the two scenarios.

"I have an idea, Mrs. Truffle!" Hazel interrupted. "How about we get a jury to decide? We can gather students from your class and teachers. That way it'll be fair and completely unbiased. If they decide that the workload is fair, then I will back off. I will never bring this up again. But, if they say that you are giving too much homework, you will assign five fewer pages per night," Hazel told her.

Mrs. Truffle put her pen down and stared down at the desk in thought. She contemplated, and the silence grew, Hazel wondered if she had crossed the line.

"We can do that…."

Hazel exhaled.

"As long as Principal Winter approves it and she picks the jurors," she responded. "You may go now, Hazel." She nodded and returned to her stack of papers.

Right after class, Hazel walked over to Principal Winter's office and peeked her head in.

"Principal Winter, do you have a minute?" Hazel went on to explain what happened in class that day and explained her idea.

"That sounds like a great and fair idea, Hazel! I am so glad you thought of it. It seems Mrs. Hansen's class paid off," Principal Winter told her. "I'll find a perfect jury."

Hazel walked out of the office, proud she was making a change.

The 8th Amendment

Excessive bail shall not be required, nor excessive fines imposed, nor cruel and unusual punishments inflicted.

Hazel and a bunch of her classmates entered the history classroom falling over from laughter. They all sat down, barely keeping it together.

"What happened to all of you?" Mrs. Hansen asked them, laughing from the state her students were in.

Hazel, still gasping for air, tried to explain what had just transpired outside the classroom.

"So…. and then… and then she fell…..hahahaha."

Mrs. Hansen, not able to understand, just shook her head, smiling, and started the class. Her rowdy students calmed down.

By the time class was over, Hazel was still in a hyper mood.

"Alright guys, you have to complete this exit ticket and then I'll let you out early," Mrs. Hansen told them.

The class groaned as one.

"You know Mrs. Hansen this could be considered excessive bail. This is unconstitutional and you shouldn't make us do this," Hazel said, joking.

Mrs. Hansen laughed at that. "Okay, how about this, I won't make you complete the exit ticket if you can accurately explain to me what the 8th amendment is."

Hazel glanced at her classmates. "Well…"

"Don't worry if you don't know. Here, let me help." Mrs. Hansen said, "The 8th amendment is that excessive bail should not be required. Let's use the exit ticket as an example. You could argue that completing the assignment to exit class was too much and it's impossible to meet."

"Ooh!" Hazel exclaimed. "Which would mean that since it was too much to do, it was excessive bail, and therefore unconstitutional. We couldn't meet the demands because they were made to make sure we couldn't."

"Exactly. Good job, Hazel. Though that doesn't apply in this case because completing the exit ticket is very simple," Mrs. Hansen explained to her students. "I will let it pass today because you learned something new. Have a good day!"

The 9th Amendment

The enumeration in the Constitution, of certain rights, shall not be construed to deny or disparage others retained by the people.

Hazel walked into school, energized, despite the heavy load of homework in her backpack weighing her down. The extra spring in her step came from a surprise from her parents: Her entire family was going on vacation to Greece! The only downside was that she had to do make-up work for school, but that was easy to deal with.

As soon as Hazel got to school she told her friends all about the trip.

"Oh my god, Hazel. You are so lucky! I wish I was going to Greece," her friend, Violet, exclaimed as they walked to history class.

"I know. It is going to be so fun!" Hazel responded as they stopped in front of their history class, eyes sparkling.

As they walked into class, Hazel went up to Mrs. Hansen, who was grading papers at her desk, excited to tell her the good news.

"Good morning, Mrs. Hansen," Hazel told her.

"Oh hello, Hazel," she said, looking up and putting her papers aside.

"So, I found out last night that I am going on vacation to Greece next week. I was wondering what makeup work

I will have to do for this class," Hazel told her, fiddling with her hands. She was dreading doing the makeup work on the ninth amendment because she knew she didn't understand it.

"Wow, that sounds like so much fun!" Mrs. Hansen told her. sitting back in her chair thinking. "You know what, just answer one question, verbally, and you don't have to do any makeup work. How does that sound?"

"Great!" Hazel said tentatively.

"Okay, here it is. You can take some time to think about it. Where in the Constitution does it say you have the right to travel?"

Hazel was confused. They had read the entire Constitution in class and it wasn't anywhere there. She spent the entire class thinking it over, getting more and more stressed. After class, Mrs. Hansen called Hazel over.

"So Hazel, did you figure it out?"

"I'm sorry Mrs. Hansen, but I don't know," Hazel regretfully told her.

"Don't worry it was meant to be hard. Here, let me give you a hint. Look in the amendments," Mrs. Hansen told her.

Hazel was taken aback. While Mrs. Hansen looked on, Hazel began to think long and hard, pondering the dilemma. Hazel began to panic as she could hear the wall clock tick as she wracked her brain.

As she mulled her lessons over in her head, she grew more confused. There was no amendment that talked about the right to travel. It wasn't the second...nor the third...as she processed the articles, an idea struck her. That was the answer! There was literally no amendment that talks about travel.

Suddenly, inspiration came flooding back to her. Some laws are not stated in the Constitution, but they just make sense to have. You can logically infer that you have them! Just like the right to travel! So the amendment would state that you can infer the right to travel.

As she continued to think about Mrs. Hansen's hint, she thought back on all the amendments with new excitement. First, Second, Third...Wait, what about the ninth amendment?

"The enumeration in the Constitution, of certain rights, shall not be construed to deny or disparage others retained by the people."

She mulled over the meaning of the dense wording. She suddenly understood that the ninth amendment was saying that some rights were not specifically stated in the Constitution, but you could assume that you had them, based on the rest of the laws. She could apply that to the right to travel! All the pieces suddenly fell into place. You can logically infer you have some rights that are not specifically mentioned. And therefore, using logic, Hazel had the right to travel. She let out a breath before speaking.

"The ninth amendment! The ninth amendment says that the rights listed in the Constitution are not your only rights. The Constitution does not state that I cannot travel and I am a citizen of the United States; therefore I have the right to travel because it is inferred through the ninth amendment. Some rights are not stated but they are there in the amendment!" Hazel exclaimed.

"You got it. Good job, Hazel. Have fun in Greece! I can't wait to hear all about it," Mrs. Hansen told her, bidding Hazel goodbye.

The 10th Amendment

The powers not delegated to the United States by the Constitution, nor prohibited by it to the States, are reserved to the States respectively, or to the people.

Hazel walked into history class in a flurry. Her last class had been a mess of equations and notes, and she was still clinging to books and paper, frantically trying to keep them in a stack. She reached her desk just in time to drop the whole stack.

"Whew!"

Mrs. Hansen looked up from the board to take in the mess of Hazel's desk. "Woah, Hazel. That's some pile you got there."

Hazel laughed slightly and began shuffling the papers into order. Mrs. Hansen stepped aside, revealing the words:

The Tenth Amendment Experiment

"Alright, class, the tenth amendment! This is the last one we will be covering, so I decided to do something different this time," Mrs. Hansen said.

Hazel raised her hand. "So exactly, what do you mean by different?"

"Hold your horses, Hazel, I'm getting to that." Mrs. Hansen laughed. "The tenth amendment states that any power that is not specifically given to the United States federal government by the Constitution is given to the people or the States. Now, that can be confusing so I am creating a little experiment that will last a week. In this experiment, I am going to be the United States government and the class is going to be the people."

Hazel, confused, raised her hand again. "But how do we know what we can decide and what you can?"

"Good question, Hazel. I have asked one of the other teachers to draft us a Constitution we will follow."

Hazel contemplated for a moment before responding. "Huh, so the Constitution will have you make some decisions but others we will have to make, just like in the United States government."

"Exactly, Hazel."

Mrs. Hansen passed out a packet to each student of their Constitution. "Here it says that I have to decide the class rules, but it doesn't say I have to assign seats. That's your job. Do you want to assign seats?"

Hazel thought about it. This was going to be a fun experiment. They were going to be a mini-United States. The tenth amendment ensured that the federal government did not have ultimate power but it got only as much as the Constitution allowed. The power that was not specifically given to the government was given to the people and states.

ABOOKS

ALIVE Book Publishing and ALIVE Publishing Group
are imprints of Advanced Publishing LLC,
3200 A Danville Blvd., Suite 204, Alamo, California 94507

Telephone: 925.837.7303
alivebookpublishing.com